Super Me 1

Fun Book

LUCIA TOMAS   VICKY GIL

Illustrations by Ben Cort

OXFORD UNIVERSITY PRESS
1997

1 My friends

4

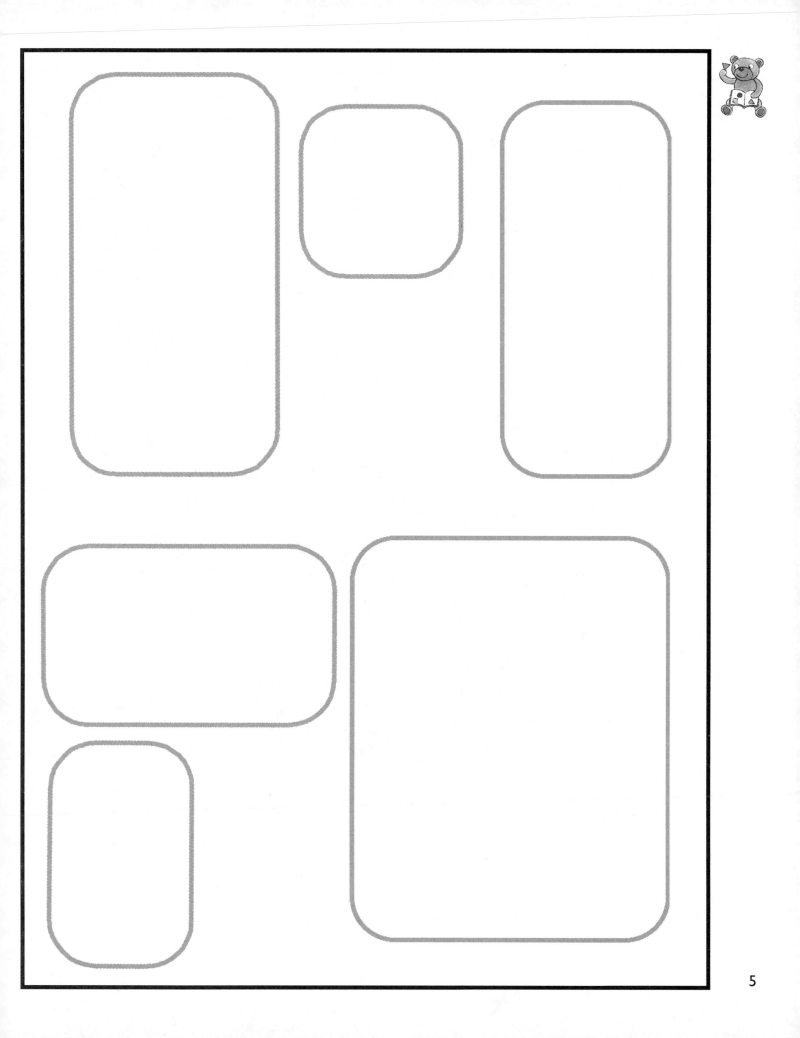

5

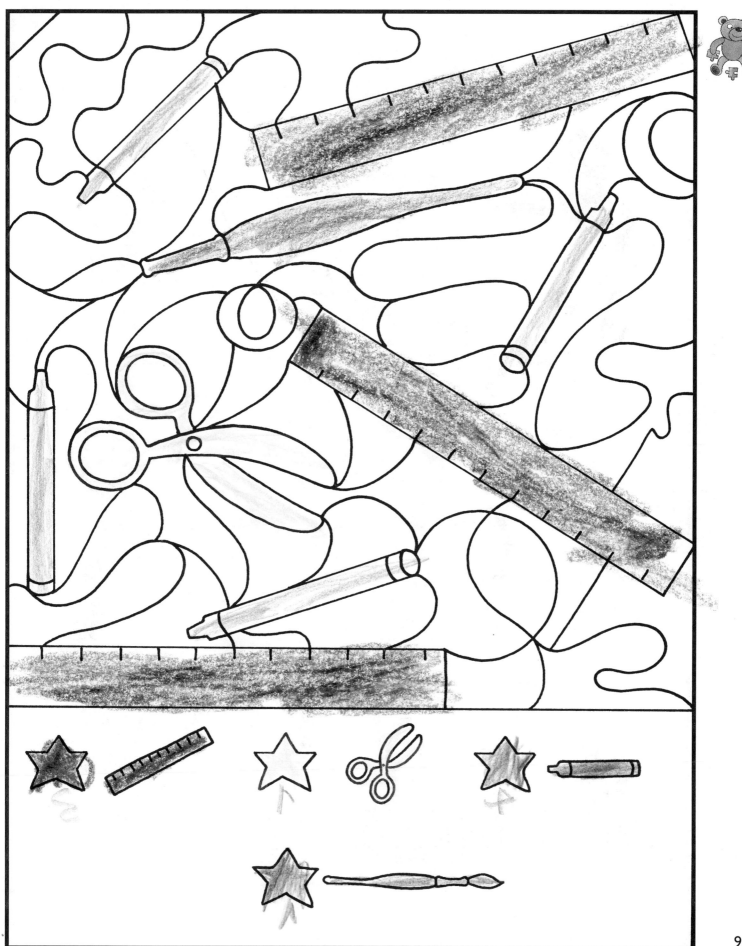

10

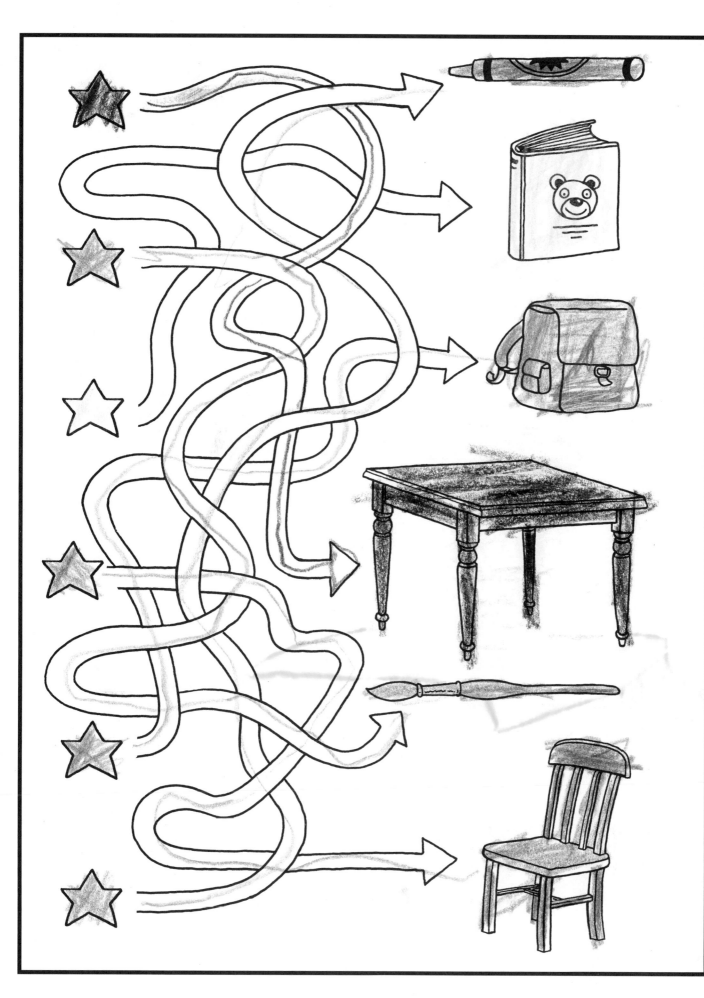

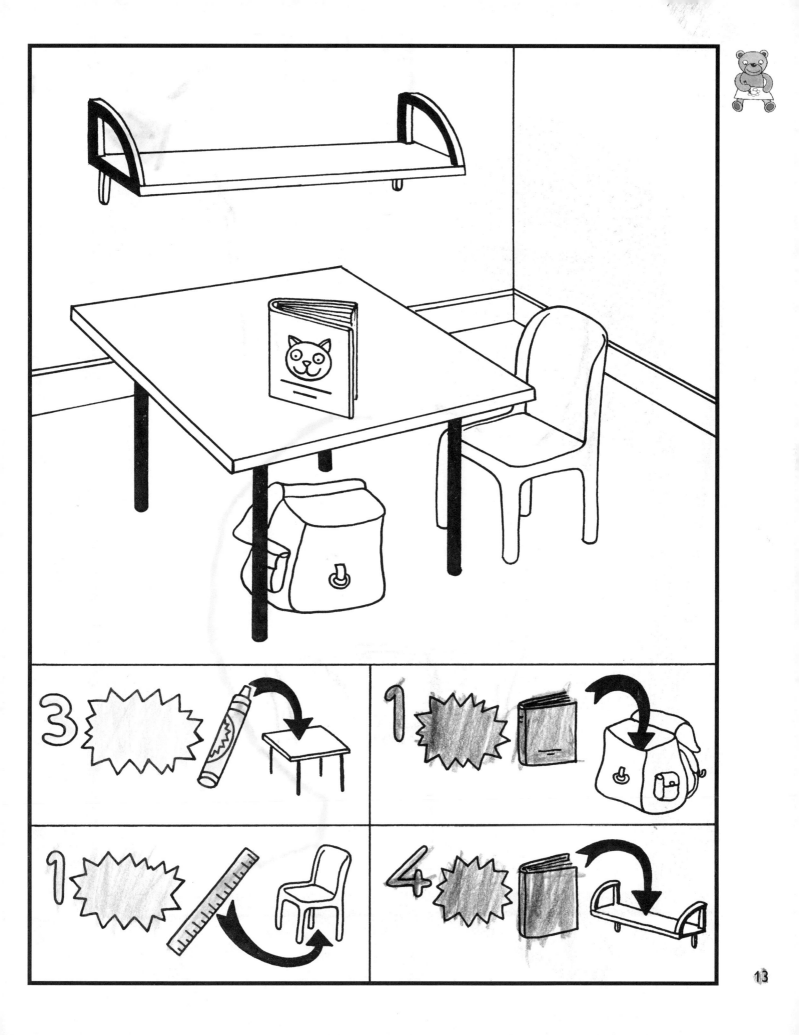

13

3 My body

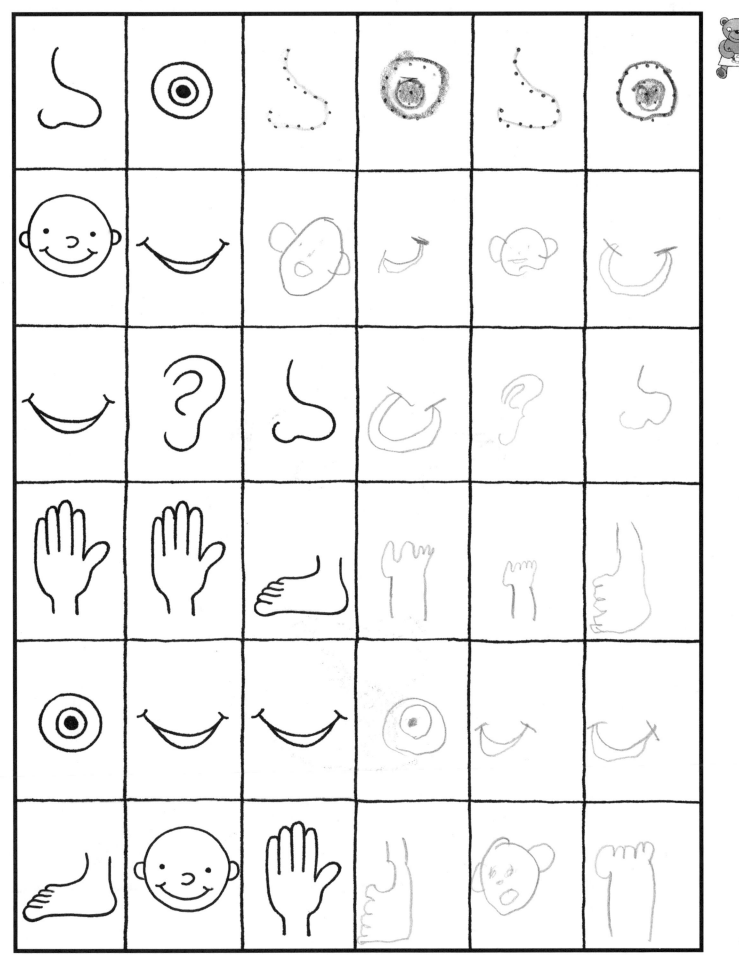

4 My home

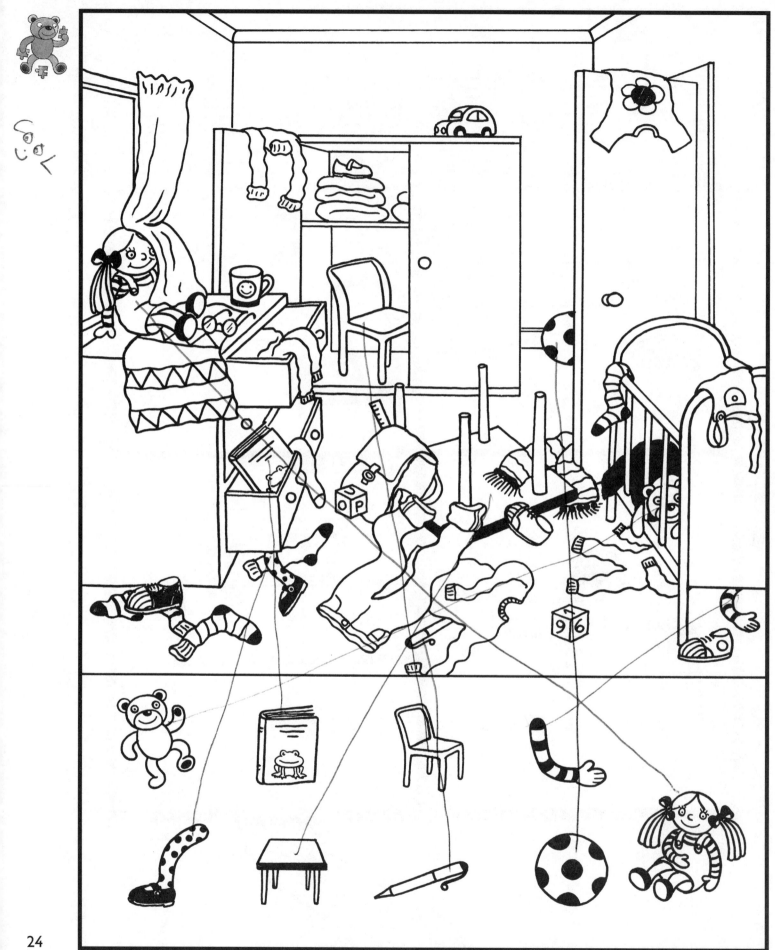

24

25

5 My pet

29

6 My food

MENU

7 My show

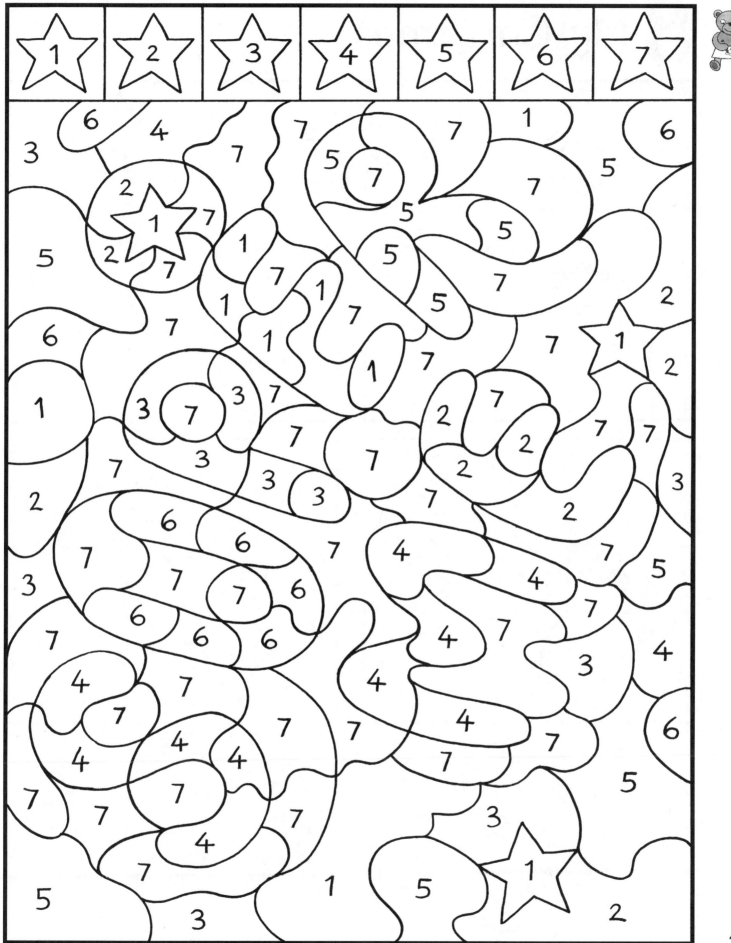

43

45

Super Songs lyrics

Five brown teddies

Five brown teddies sitting on a wall,
Five brown teddies sitting on a wall,
And if one brown teddy
Should accidentally fall,
There'd be four brown teddies
Sitting on the wall.

Four brown teddies sitting on a wall...
Three brown teddies sitting on a wall...
Two brown teddies sitting on a wall...

One brown teddy sitting on a wall,
One brown teddy sitting on a wall,
And if one brown teddy
Should accidentally fall,
There'd be no brown teddies
Sitting there at all!

Sing a rainbow

Red and yellow
And pink and green,
Purple and orange and blue.
I can sing a rainbow,
Sing a rainbow,
Sing a rainbow, too.

Wind the bobbin up

Wind the bobbin up,
Wind the bobbin up,
Pull, pull, clap, clap, clap.
Point to the ceiling,
Point to the floor,
Point to the window,
Point to the door.
Clap your hands together,
One, two, three,
Put you hands down on your knee.

Ten in the bed

There were ten in the bed
And the little one said,
'Roll over! Roll over!'
So they all rolled over
And one fell out...

There were nine in the bed...
There were eight in the bed...
There were seven in the bed...
There were six in the bed...
There were five in the bed...
There were four in the bed...
There were three in the bed...
There were two in the bed...

There was one in the bed
And no one said,
'Roll over! Roll over!'
So no one rolled over
And no one fell out!

Clap your hands

Clap your hands, clap your hands,
Clap them just like me.
Touch your shoulders, touch your shoulders,
Touch them just like me.
Tap your knees, tap your knees,
Tap them just like me.
Shake your head, shake your head,
Shake it just like me.
Clap your hands, clap your hands.
Then let them quiet be.

Head, shoulders, knees, and toes

Head, shoulders, knees, and toes, knees and toes,
Head, shoulders, knees, and toes, knees and toes.
Eyes and ears and mouth and nose,
Head, shoulders, knees and toes, knees and toes.

Miss Polly had a dolly

Miss Polly had a dolly
Who was sick, sick, sick,
So she phoned for the doctor
To come quick, quick, quick.
The doctor came
With her bag and her hat
And she knocked at the door
With a rat, tat, tat.

She looked at the dolly
And she shook her head,
And she said 'Miss Polly,
Put her straight to bed.'
She wrote on a paper
For a pill, pill, pill.
'I'll be back in the morning
With my bill, bill, bill.'

In a cottage in a wood

In a cottage in a wood,
A little man at the window stood.
He saw a rabbit running by,
Knocking at the door.

'Help me, help me,' the rabbit said,
'Before the hunter shoots me dead!'

'Come little rabbit, come with me.
Happy we shall be.'

Two little dicky birds sitting on a wall

Two little dicky birds
Sitting on a wall.
One named Peter,
One named Paul.

Fly away Peter,
Fly away Paul.
Come back Peter,
Come back Paul.

Five currant buns

Five currant buns in a baker's shop,
Round and fat with sugar on the top.
Along came a boy with a penny one day,
Bought a currant bun and took it away.

Four currant buns, etc.
Three currant buns, etc.
Two currant buns, etc.

One currant bun in a baker's shop,
Round and fat with sugar on the top.
Along came a boy with a penny one day,
Bought the currant bun and took it away.

One potato, two potatoes

One potato, two potatoes,
Three potatoes, four,
Five potatoes, six potatoes,
Seven potatoes, more.
O-U-T spells out
So out you must go!

Pat-a-cake

Pat-a-cake, pat-a-cake, baker's man,
Bake me a cake as fast as you can.
Pat it and prick it and mark it with 'B'
And put it in the oven for baby and me.

Oh, we can play the big bass drum

Oh, we can play the big bass drum
And this is the way we do it.
BOOM, BOOM, BOOM goes the big bass drum
And that's the way we do it.

Oh, we can play the violin
And this is the way we do it.
FIDDLE-DIDDLE-DEE goes the violin
And that's the way we do it.

Oh, we can play the triangle
And this is the way we do it.
TING, TING, TING goes the triangle
And that's the way we do it.

Oh, we can play the silver flute
And this is the way we do it.
TOOTLE-OOTLE-OOT goes the silver flute
And that's the way we do it.

A witch came flying

A witch came flying, flying, flying,
A witch came flying, flying, flying,
A witch came flying all on a summer's day.

A clown came dancing, dancing, dancing,
A clown came dancing, dancing, dancing,
A clown came dancing all on a summer's day.

A king came marching, marching, marching,
A king came marching, marching, marching,
A king came marching all on a summer's day.

A wolf came running, running, running,
A wolf came running, running, running,
A wolf came running all on a summer's day.

I sent a letter to my love

I sent a letter to my love
And on the way I dropped it.
One of you has picked it up
And put it in your pocket.

O Christmas tree

O Christmas tree, O Christmas tree,
How lovely are your branches.
O Christmas tree, O Christmas tree,
How lovely are your branches.

In summer sun or winter snow
A coat of green you always show.
O Christmas tree, O Christmas tree,
How lovely are your branches.

2 Stevie's story

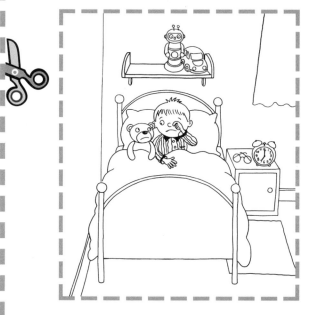

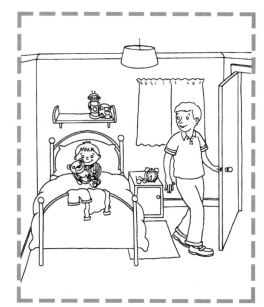

3 Baby's story

4 Annie's story

5 Fluffy's story

6 Lucy's story

7 Our show

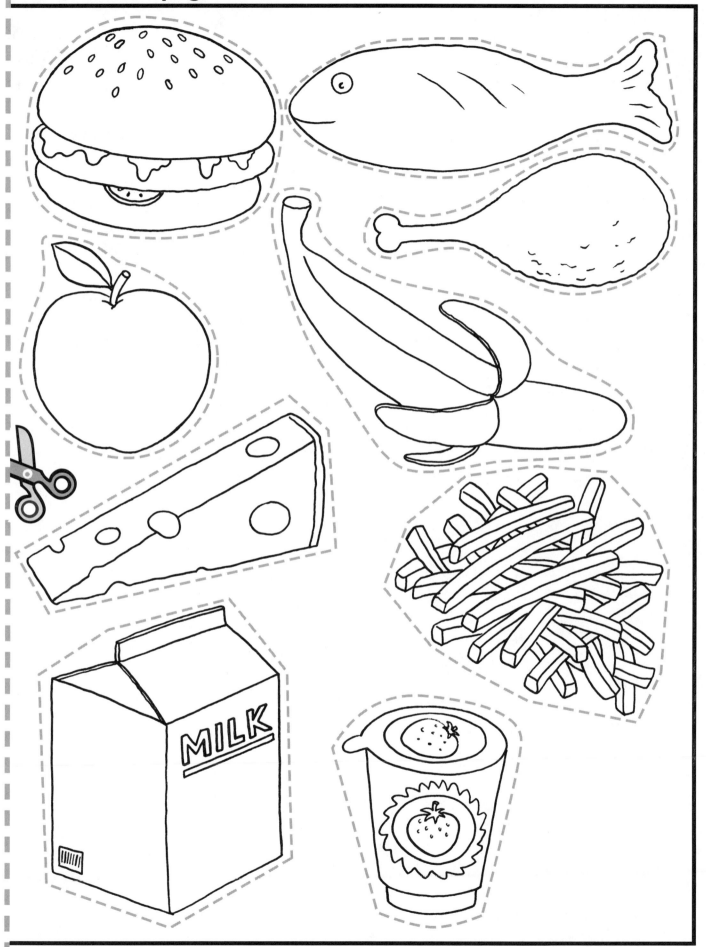